· THE JOY OF AVERY SERIES ·

BRAVER THAN ME

RHONDA WAGNER
ILLUSTRATED BY KIMBERLY GROVES

LUCIDBOOKS

To
Avery,
my loquacious granddaughter, who brings so much joy.

And, to her parents,
Lisa and JJ,
who obeyed God's call to become foster parents.

And especially,
to
our Heavenly Father,
who can be trusted to write the most beautiful stories for our lives,
"more than all we can ask or imagine" (Ephesians 3:20)!

In memory of my sister,
Kim,
who was always so much braver than me.

Read more of this family's story of foster care and their
mission to provide hope and encouragement at
www.messintoamessage.com,
or follow on Instagram @lisa_messintoamessage.

Mom's phone rang. Avery wondered if it was The Call.

Mom and Dad had been official for three months, but they were still waiting for The Call that would make them a foster family.

The bedroom next to Avery's room was ready. A special pillow decorated the bed.

Avery gave it a big squeezy hug. One day, another child would sleep here— Avery's foster sibling.

She wondered if the foster child would be scared to sleep somewhere new, even with a special pillow.

"Avery! That was The Call!" Mom shouted.
Avery ran downstairs.

"A three-year-old boy named Zander is
coming today." Mom said.

"We've got to go!"

2

"If he's coming, why are we going, Mom?" Avery asked as she tugged on her boots.

Mom laughed. "That does sound silly! We need to buy a few things for Zander before he arrives."

3

At the store, Avery stomped snow from her boots. Mom grabbed a cart.
"Can I pick out a toy for Zander?" Avery asked.
"Great idea!" Mom said. "And let's find him warm footy pajamas for these cold nights."

4

Soon the cart was full of pajamas, underwear, diapers, socks, mittens, snacks, a sippy cup, and the softest teddy bear Avery could find.

"In case he gets scared," Avery told Mom.

Instead of chatting on the drive home,
Avery wondered about Zander.

She felt excited to meet him.

Would Zander like car rides on little roads like she did?
Big roads made Avery too sleepy to talk, and she loved to talk.

6

Mom remarked, "My loquacious girl is quiet today, even on these little roads."
So many questions were tangled up inside Avery's head until . . .

. . . they all tumbled out!

"Mom, do you think Zander will like our family?

Does he like teddy bears? He can cuddle his teddy bear if he's scared.

Will he play in the snow with me?

Does he like cats? We have lots of cats!

Maybe he likes dogs better.

Or fish?

Or birds?

Does he have a favorite color?

A favorite food?

A favorite shirt?

What will it be like when Zander has to say goodbye?"

"Whoa, Avery!" **Mom chuckled.** "So many questions! We only know his name and age. We will learn about Zander's favorite things day by day.

Let's be brave as a new foster family. We are in this together."

At home, Avery watched at
the door for Dad's arrival.

"Brrrrr, it's cold out there," Dad said.
"Are you ready to be a Big Sister, Avery?"

She took a deep breath.
"I'm ready, Dad.
I'm going to be brave."

"I know you will," said Dad.
"If I had a Big Sister, I would want
her to be just like you!"

"He's here!"
cried Mom.

"Okay, let's make Zander
feel welcome."

Dad opened the door. A woman from the foster care agency stepped inside carrying a little boy bundled in a blue blanket. Avery noticed the boy had no coat or boots.

"Hello, Zander," Mom said with outstretched arms.

"Mama," he whimpered.

Mom scooped him close. "Do you miss your mama? This is Avery. We are her parents, and we will take good care of you both."

Zander looked at Avery with sad brown eyes.

"This is your teddy," said Avery, handing him the fuzzy bear she picked out at the store. "I cuddle my teddy when I am scared."

Zander gave teddy a big squeezy hug.

Avery smiled.

Dad introduced Zander to their cats, Jaxon and Lola.
"Meow. Kitties," Zander said.
"He likes cats!" said Avery.

Mom filled Zander's new sippy cup and made a tray of snacks.

"These are Avery's favorites, Zander.
We want to learn your favorites, too," said Mom.

Avery grabbed a yogurt pouch. "Squeeze it like this, Zander."

Zander squeezed. "Yummy!"

Together they ate until they were full.

On their first night as a foster family, Mom stayed in Zander's room while he fell asleep.

Dad put Avery to bed.
"Teddy will help Zander feel brave," said Avery.

"It's a great gift!" Dad agreed.

"I would be scared to leave home," said Avery.

"Well, you won't be leaving us," Dad assured her. "You are safe. Zander needs a safe home right now until his home is safe again. If possible, we hope for . . ."

Avery interrupted to say, "Re-uni-ca-fation!"

"Yes, re-uni-fi-cation." said Dad, nodding.

14

Avery knew it meant Zander could go home to his family one day.
Until then, he would be part of their family.

Avery fell asleep dreaming of things
they would do together.

One morning, Mom planned a visit to the library. Nana was going, too.

"You'll like it, Zander, but we have to whisper," Avery said.

"Like this? Shhhhh." Zander put his finger to his mouth like Avery.

"Yes, like that," said Mom. "Let's have a snack before we go."

"Pop and noo-nules?" asked Zander.

"We have juice, milk, or water," Mom answered.
"And no time to cook noodles."

"No cook," Zander said, finding a box in the pantry.
Mom pulled out a piece of uncooked pasta.

"Yum!" Zander said, grabbing the stick to chomp.

"Can I try one?" Avery asked.

"Yes! Noo-nules are yummy," said Zander.
He handed one to Avery.

Mom smiled. "I guess I'll join you two."
She took a crunchy bite.

Zander felt happy. Together they munched
on his favorite snack before leaving.

Inside the library, they stopped first at the fish tank.
Zander pointed at a large goldfish.

"Glub! Glub!" he said.

"Mom, he likes fish!" Avery liked learning Zander's favorite things.

Nana took their picture.

"Everyone smile! And say,
'Glub!
Glub!'"

In the play area, another mother walked up to Avery's mom.

"Is that Zander?" she whispered. Mom was surprised she knew Zander. The woman introduced herself and said, "I was his foster mother."

A young boy came near. Zander recognized them. "Mama! Isaac!" They both gave Zander a big squeezy hug!

The two mothers talked while Avery, Zander, and Isaac played at a table with Nana.

That night, Avery asked Dad why Zander had lived with another foster family.

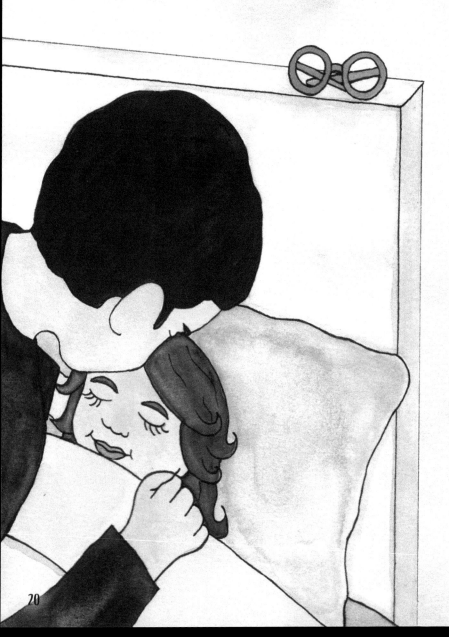

"His birth parents needed help more than once," Dad answered.

"Zander is so brave, Dad," remarked Avery.

"Yes, he is," Dad agreed. "And so are you."

"Thanks!" Avery said. "I love being Zander's sister in our foster family."

"It feels good to give our best love to another person around here," Dad said as he kissed her goodnight, and Avery agreed.

Avery adored being a Big Sister.
She taught Zander how to make snow angels.

"Lay down and flap your
arms like a bird,"

Avery demonstrated.

"And your legs, too!"

"Chirp! Chirp!" sang Zander.

Avery smiled.

She added birds and snow to
Zander's list of favorite things.

They rolled snowballs to
make a snowman.
Avery lifted Zander to place
the carrot nose.

Later, Avery thought about the changes that came as a foster family. Someone was always knocking at their door.

Friends brought gifts for Zander or dinner for the whole family. Avery and Zander liked desserts best!

Agency people stopped by to see how their family was doing. Zander was happy to show them his teddy and his bed with the special pillow.

On Fridays, Zander visited his birth parents at the agency.

Avery missed him while he was gone.

She could hardly remember feeling nervous about Zander's arrival. Now, she only wondered how hard it would be to say goodbye.

Avery decided the best change of all was having Zander to love.

One day, while Zander was napping, Mom's phone rang.

After that call, Avery looked at Mom's teary eyes,
and she knew Zander was leaving.

"It's a happy-and-sad-at-the-same-time thing, Avery," Mom said.
"We love Zander, but it's good he can go home."

Avery fought tears and nodded.
"Will we see him again?"

"Hopefully," Mom replied.
"I'll put our phone number on a note to his mom."

That night, Avery watched Mom pack Zander's things.
She folded his favorite shirt with the red stripes, his favorite color.

Then their family prayed for Zander and his family.

The next morning, an agency woman pulled into the driveway.

Dad, Mom, and Avery gave Zander an extra-special, really big squeezy hug.
When they finally let go, they let their tears flow.

Zander took the woman's hand and walked to the car.
He turned back to wave.

"I'll look for you at the library!" shouted Avery.

Dad patted Avery's head as Zander drove away.

"My Brave Ave," said Dad.

"Thanks," Avery said, wiping tears from her cheeks.

"But Zander was braver than me.
He was always braver than me."

Dear Reader,

I hope you like my story so far and will tell your friends about it because more people need to know about foster care! More moms and dads should go to school to become foster parents like mine. There are so many children who need a place to live where families will give their best love. And, the rules really aren't so bad.

If you and your parents are thinking about becoming a foster family, be brave, and contact a local agency soon. You are in this together, so you don't have to worry about it. But it's okay to wonder.

With love and joy,

Avery

Glossary

Birth parents — parents a child was born to.

Foster care agency — trained group of individuals who oversee formal care, placement, and protection of children.

Foster child — child who is being cared for in the home of foster parents rather than in their own parents' home for a while.

Foster family — a family who has at least one foster child in the home.

Foster parents — people who officially take a child into their family for a while without becoming the child's legal parents.

Foster sibling — a foster child being raised by your parents.

Loquacious — talkative, chatty (someone like Avery).

Official — formally licensed by the county to be foster parents.

Reunification — a foster child goes home to his or her birth family (sometimes pronounced re-uni-ca-fation).

Whimpered — made quiet sounds due to sadness, pain, or fear.

Conversation Starters

First Placement Call (pages 1–5)

When the first call comes, placement may be quick and happen with little information. It's always nice to have something special for the child's arrival.

- Would you like to pick something out for our first foster child, like Avery did?

Your Biological* Child's Feelings & Questions (pages 8–9, 14, 20)

Talk through as many questions as you can before the foster child arrives. More questions will come later. Assure your child(ren) of their own safety and your love for them.

- What makes you feel safe and loved? Let's treat your new foster sibling that way.

Birth Order (page 10)

Foster families have the option to preserve the birth order of their biological* children or to mix it up as foster children come and go within their family. Choose the best dynamic for your family.

- What did Avery's dad mean when he asked whether she was ready to be a Big Sister?

A Foster Child's Arrival (page 11)

Advise your child(ren) to be calm when a foster child arrives. This child's world has just turned upside down. A house full of commotion may be overwhelming.

Age-appropriately talk through what removals may be like for children. They may be taken quickly from their home for safety concerns, allowing no time to pack a bag or even grab a coat or shoes.

- Aren't you glad the woman from the foster care agency wrapped Zander in a warm blanket?

Conditions to Consider in Fostering a Child (page 11)

All foster parents complete a form choosing conditions they feel able to accept in a child placement—age, gender, race, medical handicaps, special needs, bed-wetting, past abuse, and so on. Prepare your biological* child(ren) with open and age-appropriate conversation, especially if accepting medically fragile children or if providing a therapeutic home.

- Would you like to talk through any questions you have about race or special needs?

Placement Outcomes & the Hard Goodbye (pages 14–15, 24–28)

Talk through the possibilities of placement length and the impact different outcomes may have on the members of your family (e.g., respite vs. long-term, reunification, kinship placement, adoption). The goodbye is often quite hard on parents and children alike. The reminder of "we are in this together" is valuable. And bravery is important for all.

- Do you think it will be both happy and sad when your foster sibling leaves us?
- How will it be happy? How will it be sad?

Removals Due to Neglect (pages 16–17)

Neglect can be a common cause for child removal. Talk through what might be hard about a child trying to do grown-up things on their own such as preparing snacks or meals.

- What kinds of snacks are easy for you to get for yourself without help?

Roles of Extended Family Members (pages 18–19)

Openly discuss involvement of extended family—expectations, preparations, background checks for child care, and more. When extended family members jump on board to love foster children unconditionally, it helps a foster family thrive.

- Are you excited for your grandparents, aunts, uncles, and cousins to meet your foster sibling?

Multiple Placements, Failed Reunifications (pages 19–20)

Age-appropriately discuss how everyone tries the best they can, but sometimes reunifications fail, and children come back into the system. When they do, the same family may not be able to take them into their home due to full capacity, no longer licensed, or in a different county, causing a new family placement. Multiple placements and failed reunifications are confusing for a child, prompting possible attachment disorders or trauma.

- We don't know about your foster sibling's other foster families, but what do we know about our family that is good for him or her?

Birth Family Visits (page 22)

Typically, foster children will visit with their birth parents weekly—sometimes, multiple times per week. Talk through how these visits might impact your family's routines.

- What do you think a birth family visit might be like for your foster sibling?

- We might drive the child to the agency for a visit. Would you like to ride along to do that? Or the child might get picked up at our home by an agency worker.

*Biological is used as an all-inclusive word for children who are permanently within a family's home, including biological, adopted, and those under legal guardianship.

Avery is a young girl who loves mysteries and surprises and her little family who lives on a little road. This very talkative child has been a Big Sister in a foster family five times (not counting short-term respite stays) and has experienced three different placement outcomes: reunification, kinship placement, and adoption.

Learn about the second foster child who comes to live at Avery's house in Book 3 of The Joy of Avery series.

It's Okay to Wonder
Book 1

Helps children understand their feelings as the family prepares their home and their hearts for foster care.

Braver Than Me
Book 2

Helps children understand their feelings when a foster child arrives, becomes part of the family, and says a hard goodbye.

Acknowledgments

Thank you,
Lisa Robertson,
for your valuable insight as a foster parent and your love as a daughter.

Thank you,
Sara Triana Mitchell,
for advocating for the reader with your outstanding edits.

Thank you,
Kimberly Groves,
for your masterful illustrations that bring this book to life.

Thank you,
Jamie Sandefer,
for your friendship and guidance to connect with Lucid Books.

And thank you to my husband,
Dan,
for lovingly giving up much of "our time" during this endeavor.

May all glory be to God in these combined efforts.

About the Author and Illustrator

Rhonda Wagner is a writer who lives with her husband in western Pennsylvania where she was born. They have two married daughters and four grandchildren who live in northeastern Ohio. She was inspired to write The Joy of Avery series when her younger daughter and son-in-law became foster parents. As a foster grandma, she is passionate about giving her very best love to all her grandchildren, foster and forever.

Find her online at www.rhondawagnerbook.com.

Kimberly Groves grew up in the beautiful mountains of West Virginia. Kim and her husband Justin enjoy raising their daughters on those same mountaintops. Art has always been a huge part of Kim's life, and she continues to follow that passion by bringing images to life with the stroke of a pencil or paintbrush.